Contents

KU-042-489

Find Your Calm

Everybody sometimes feels worried, scared, or anxious. There's a good reason for these feelings—they can help us to protect ourselves, and to stay safe and unharmed.

It is perfectly normal to get nervous if you are faced with unusual situations or stressful surroundings. Sometimes, though, your body feels this way even when there's nothing to worry about. You can feel more anxious than necessary even though you are perfectly safe.

Anxious feelings can affect your thoughts, body, and actions. Learning to recognize and manage your anxious feelings is a life-long journey. When you learn to tune into them, you can gain control and find your calm.

Find Your Calm

by Dr. Katie O'Connell
and Lisa Regan

ARCTURUS

For kids and parents finding their calm,
and for Lisa who found me.

This edition published in 2020 by Arcturus Publishing Limited
26/27 Bickels Yard, 151–153 Bermondsey Street,
London SE1 3HA

Authors: Dr. Katie O'Connell and Lisa Regan
Illustrator: Mel Howells
Editor: Donna Gregory
Designer: Jeni Child
Editorial Manager: Joe Harris
Design Manager: Jessica Holliland

ISBN: 978-1-78950-648-8
CH007199NT
Supplier 29, Date 0320, Print run 10174

Printed in China

Anxiety can show itself in different ways. You might start to breathe faster or sweat. Your muscles might tense up and borrow oxygen from your brain, making you feel wobbly or dizzy. Feeling like this can stop you from enjoying the things you want to. It is important to learn about your feelings and be able to deal with them.

When you have sad feelings, it's really important to notice them. Don't try to ignore them as they will hang around for longer. What might make you feel better? Sometimes just a hug can help. Other times, you might need to talk it through.

This book gives you the tools to manage your feelings and guide you through tough situations.

Who can help you?

You don't have to struggle alone. Learning to manage your feelings is part of growing up. Nearly everyone you know, including your parents and teachers, has felt like you feel now (whatever that might be) at some point.

Don't be afraid to bring up your struggles with people you trust. This can be a relative, sibling, friend, teacher, or coach. Sometimes hearing about how other people manage their feelings gives us good ideas about what we can try and also helps us to not feel alone. It can be hard at first, but once you bring it up you will discover that many other people are working on finding their calm.

Set Yourself Some Feeling Goals

Sometimes it helps to put into words what you want to achieve.

Apart from being calm, what would you like to feel? Here are some examples:

- I want to sleep well.

- I want to be brave.

- I want to be able to deal with changes.

- I want to be able to concentrate.

- I want to be better at coping with new situations.

- I want to get rid of some nervous energy.

- I want to calm my mind and my body.

Write down one or two feeling goals that really matter to you here:

Write down something that has affected your feelings recently:

_____

_____

_____

If you're finding it hard to think of connections between things that have happened and how you've been feeling, here are some examples:

- **You might feel nervous about starting a new school.**

- You might feel proud if you tried something new.

- You might feel upset if somebody you love has gone away.

- You might feel relieved if you did well on a test.

Can you think of something that you can do to help you achieve one of your feeling goals?

_____

_____

How it helps

Knowing the connections between your feelings, thoughts, and actions brings you closer to being your super-smart, reflective self. Setting feeling goals is just as important as setting goals in any other area of your life. Set your own targets for how you want to feel and behave.

Adjust the Dial

Everybody's mood changes during the day. One minute you're bobbing along just fine, and then the next minute you feel fizzy, fidgety, shaky, frustrated, unbalanced, or worried about something. It's perfectly natural, because your mind is sending your body messages to adapt to demands.

Learn to listen to your body and tune in to how you're feeling. Think of your emotions like a thermostat that you can adjust up and down to keep yourself comfortable, with rising and falling temperatures. What is the point where you feel calm, balanced, and content? Notice that as your sense of calm fades, your dial turns round from calm blue to anxious red. As your balanced mood disappears, the anxious feelings rise. Sometimes it only goes up a little bit, but other times it might reach boiling point.

Take time out to bring your mood "temperature" back to calm again. Imagine yourself turning the dial down, slowly but surely. Keep working until you find the setting that brings you comfort. Use the activities in this book to help you turn the dial.

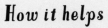

How it helps

Homeostasis is that "just right" condition when everything in your body is in balance and you feel calm. Visualizing calm gives you skills to reset yourself to a comfortable, balanced state.

Listen to Your Body

Your body has chemicals inside that can effect the way you feel and how you react to situations. The chemicals are there to help you survive; they make you run faster, think quicker, and get a buzz from doing the right thing. The chemicals show themselves on the inside and the outside of your body.

Are any of these familiar sensations?

☐ Dizzy	☐ Relaxed	☐ Annoyed
☐ Excited	☐ Shaky	☐ Loose
☐ Tingly	☐ Cold	☐ Bubbly
☐ Irritated	☐ Fuzzy	☐ Light
☐ Fluttery	☐ Calm	☐ Solid
☐ Jiggly	☐ Quiet	☐ Sick
☐ Sweaty	☐ Warm	☐ Soft
☐ Scared	☐ Numb	☐ Tense

Can you write what you think the six children on these pages are experiencing on the lines by their pictures? Are they feeling more than one thing? Ask your parent or friend if they think the same thing.

The Big Body Test

Does your whole body feel the same?
Or do different emotions affect different parts of you?
Be your own doctor and do a body scan to check yourself out.

Are you ready to have a conversation with your body, both inside and out?

Lie down and close your eyes in a room where you feel comfortable. Imagine your body is talking to you. What is it saying?

Which bits of you feel tingly, or clammy, or cold, or fizzy? Can you make a body map here? Make up your own symbols to show the different signals your body is sending.

For example, this boy is angry. It feels to him like an explosion in his head. This girl looks happy, but she is nervous. She knows this because it feels like she has butterflies fluttering in her belly.

How it helps

Sometimes our bodies know more than our thinking minds do.
Your heart, lungs, muscles, and skin are good at telling you how they feel.
These things all work without needing you to tell them to, but you can also
control them around if you choose to.

Get a Move On

Your heart beats slowly when you're still, and speeds up with exercise. Put it to the test and see how it responds.

First, sit still. Put your first two fingers at the side of your neck, under your jaw. Can you feel the blip-blip-blip of your pulse? That is your heart telling you how hard it is working.

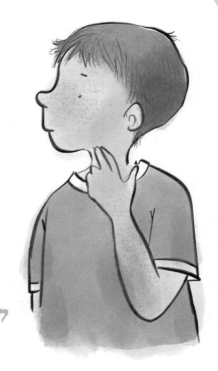

When you can feel a steady pulse, set a timer for 10 seconds. Count how many pulses you can feel. If you multiply that number by 6, you know how many times your heart beats in one minute.

Now stand up and do 25 jumping jacks, and then measure your heart rate again. It should be a higher number, because your heart is working harder.

Keep your fingers on your pulse and feel it slow down as you rest again. See how you're in control of the way your body behaves? What other activities do you do that make your heart beat faster? How long does it take to slow right back down to your resting rate?

How it helps

Your heart rate is one of the first signals of anger, threat, or upset. By getting good at feeling your heart rate you will know how keyed up or relaxed your body and mind are, and then you can work to bring it down. Learning to observe your heart rate can bring you a sense of strength and control.

Heart rate
at rest:
_____

How I moved:
_____
_____

Heart rate
after exercise:
_____

Breathe It Out

Learning to control your breathing can have a calming effect. Pretend it's your birthday and let's celebrate!

Sit somewhere comfortable and quiet. Lift your shoulders so your back is straight. Hold up your hand in front of you with your fingers gently stretched out. Imagine each one is a candle on your cake. Breathe in deeply through your nose, ready to blow them out. Feel the breath enter your belly and fill it up.

Now slowly breathe out through your mouth and blow out your first candle. Fold your finger on to your palm as you reach the end of the breath. Repeat four more times to blow out all of your candles.

Another good breathing trick is to breathe into a belly balloon. Sit quietly and close your eyes. Take a minute to just observe your breathing right now. Do you breathe in through your nose or mouth? How do you breathe out?

Now let's take control of your breathing. Put your hands on your belly and close your eyes. Imagine your belly is a balloon. Breathe in slowly through your nose to fill your belly balloon. Push out your belly until it is big and full.

Now breathe out through your mouth and let your balloon go small again. Repeat this four times. How do you feel now?

How it helps

Strong feelings can trigger physical reactions from head to toe. But you are not helpless. Breathing is the easiest and most effective way of managing your feelings. Regulating your breathing will regulate your heartbeat, your muscle tension, and strength, help you focus, and give you a sense of peace.

Body Boost

Anxiety affects your muscles, but remember who's in charge of your body. You are! Try focusing on different muscle groups using the CALM workout.

C is for Chest: First, lift your shoulders up to your ears as if you are shrugging. Now open your arms out behind you and gently push your chest forward, pulling your shoulders out and back.

A is for Arms: Now you're going to be a boxer. Punch forward, left-right-left-right, for 20 jabs. Repeat, but punching up toward the ceiling, as fast as you can. That should work up a sweat!

L is for Legs: Stand up and assume a boxing stance. Hold your fists up to your chin, and kick your left leg forward like you are kicking a door closed. Put your foot back on the floor, shift your weight to your left leg and kick your right leg back like you are a horse kicking mud off its hoof. Switch legs, and repeat.

M is for Mouth: Start with your face relaxed. Breathe in through your nose, and then stick out your tongue and breathe out while you roar like a lion. Try to stretch your tongue to your chin. Do it a few times if it feels good!

How it helps

Your muscles respond to your feelings without you knowing it. Sometimes they get stuck in a tense state. By intentionally contracting your muscles really hard, and then releasing them, you are burning the tension out of them and resetting them to be relaxed and calm.

Scan Your Skin

From sweating and blushing to goosebumps and chills, your skin can reveal giveaways to your emotions. You can see your own skin, and touch it ... but can you FEEL it?

First, check in with your feet.
You can do it with your shoes on or off,
it's up to you. How do your feet feel?
Are they tingly, or warm, sweaty, or
comfortable?

Now think about the rest of your body. What reactions take place in your skin? Do you get goosebumps? What makes them happen? What makes your hairs stand on end, your neck feel itchy, or your chest flush red? You see, your skin sends all kinds of messages about what's going on beneath the surface.

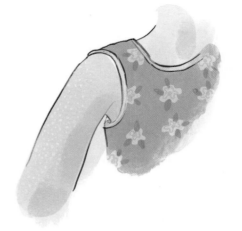

How it helps

Tuning in to a specific part of your body (your skin, heart, muscles, or lungs, as on the previous pages) can help you really focus on the way your feelings affect you physically.

Weather the Storm

Your mood will change from day to day, from morning to evening, perhaps even from one hour to the next. It's even more changeable than the weather!

Stop and think about how you feel right now. It can be hard to find the words. Instead, describe yourself like the weather. Are you feeling stormy, or sunny, or frosty, or gusty? Can you match these common feelings to these weather types?

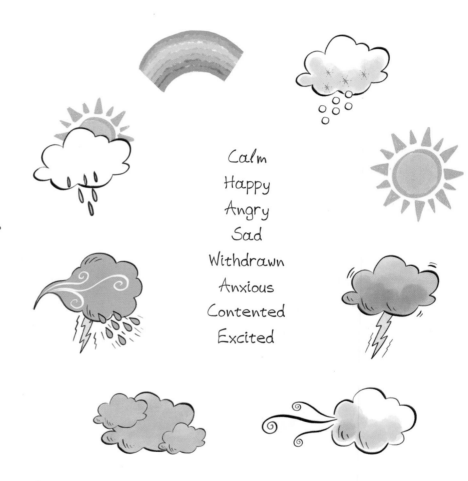

Calm
Happy
Angry
Sad
Withdrawn
Anxious
Contented
Excited

Note—there are no wrong answers here. Some people love thunderstorms, but they make some people feel very anxious. Think only about how they make YOU feel.

How it helps

Feelings are signals. Being able to label your feelings is the first step in understanding them. Knowing them helps you to be flexible and balanced so that you can make an action plan to strengthen your sunny moods. Use your knowledge to steer your fears, anger, and sadness toward happiness, balance, and peace.

Draw your feelings on the chart and see how they change over a few days. Can you see any patterns?

	Morning	Afternoon	Evening
Monday			
Tuesday			
Wednesday			
Thursday			
Friday			
Saturday			
Sunday			

Animal Instincts

Let's use some of the planet's most amazing animals to help get rid of any unsettling feelings that you have bubbling up inside.

First, you're going to breathe like a snake. Stand up nice and tall. Breathe in through your nose and feel the breath move down into your belly. Now breathe out through your front teeth, making a snakey hissing noise: "SSSSSSSSSSS." Try it again, and this time see if you can hiss for even longer.

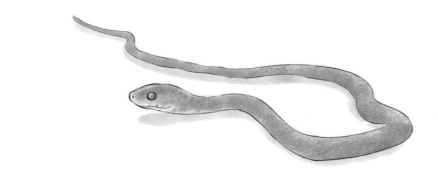

How it helps

Controlling your breath is a great way to calm your emotions and be in charge of your feelings. Practice and learn to control your breath at home, and you will be able to use it as a calming technique wherever you are.

Now it's time to breathe like a whale. Again, sit or stand straight and comfortably. Breathe in deeply through your nose. Count to five and hold that breath. Now lift your chin and tilt back your head. Imagine you are blowing your breath out through your blowhole, like a spout. Exhale hard through your mouth and empty as much breath as you can.

Be a Nature Detective

Being cooped up indoors is enough to make anyone feel restless. Head outside and let the wonder of nature soothe you.

See how many items you can spot from the detective lists here. Tick them off as you spot them. Remember, if you do touch things outdoors, wash your hands after.

The 5-4-3-2-1 list

- [ ] 5 pebbles
- [ ] 4 leaves
- [ ] 3 kinds of bark
- [ ] 2 nutshells
- [ ] 1 twig

The super spotter's list

- [ ] An animal home entrance (don't disturb the animal by looking inside or touching the home)
- [ ] A bird's nest up high
- [ ] A black stone
- [ ] A footprint
- [ ] Animal fur on a fence
- [ ] A feather
- [ ] Moss on a tree
- [ ] A fallen log
- [ ] A purple flower
- [ ] A plant that's taller than you

Get involved with the nature that you see. Touch the bark of different trees and compare how they feel. Can you find a smooth trunk, and a really bumpy one? Does it change texture from low down to higher up the tree? How does the bark on the branches feel?

How it helps

Engaging with nature has an almost instant calming effect. Looking at small details, and focusing on a single sense such as touch, can concentrate your brain and shift your emotions away from a wound-up state.

Push it!

Is something making you angry? Let's get your body
moving to get rid of those feelings.

Stand up straight, facing a wall. Put your hands out in
front of you and push against the wall. Go on—PUSH!
Push as hard as you can, as if you are trying to push
it over. Push for 10 seconds, stop, and then push again.
Repeat one more time.

If you like how this feels, you
could do a few push-ups, too.
Get on your hands and knees,
and then walk your feet back
until your legs are straight
and you're balanced on your
hands and feet. Your body
should be in a straight line
from head to heels, and your
hands directly under your
shoulders. Keeping your body
perfectly straight, lower your
body down to the ground and
back up again.

Ribbon dancing is a great way to get your arms moving. Tie a 2-m (7-ft) piece of bright ribbon to a short stick. Go outside, make sure there's lots of space around you so you don't hit anything or anyone, and then draw really big shapes with the ribbons. Can you "air-write" your name?

How it helps

Using your muscles releases feel-good chemicals into your body. Doing physical work is a great way to let off steam when you might otherwise feel like lashing out.

Feeling Blue?

Use blue food to get rid of a blue mood! If you don't like blueberries, use different berries.

1 You will need a box of vanilla cupcake or muffin mix. You will also need a small container of fresh or frozen blueberries.

2 Make up the batter according to the directions on the box.

3 Take your time adding the berries to the bowl. Stir them in slowly and watch as the juices swirl through the batter. Can you make a spiral? Does the batter turn purple?

4 Spoon the mixture into the muffin cases. Think about your body as you do this. It's easy to hold your breath as you concentrate. Don't! Keep breathing as you scoop and pour, scoop and pour. Don't forget to lick the bowl!

5 Bake the cakes as instructed on the box. Now comes the big test—can you wait long enough for them to cool before you eat your first one?

Take a photograph of your baking and send it or show it to someone you love. Write down any nice things they say about your masterpiece.

Stick a picture of your baking triumph here!

How it helps

Stirring and pouring are both soothing actions. Watching the spirals of purple appear and then get swallowed up is also good for relieving anxious feelings.

Talking to Yourself

Sometimes negative thoughts get on top of you. Learn to replace them with positive ones that help you believe in your best self.

You can think positive thoughts no matter where you are. Repeat them in your head if you're on the bus, at school, or in any public place. Say them out loud to yourself (or to a stuffed animal!) if you're alone. Write them down and doodle around them to make them pretty or fun. The important thing is to repeat them each day to help them lodge in your head and have a positive effect.

- [ ] I am calm
- [ ] I am kind
- [ ] I can try new things
- [ ] I am brave
- [ ] I can cope
- [ ] I can do it!
- [ ] I am a good friend
- [ ] I work hard
- [ ] I am loved
- [ ] My mind is quiet
- [ ] I love myself

- [ ] I am proud of myself
- [ ] I am healthy
- [ ] I trust myself
- [ ] My body is relaxed
- [ ] I am safe
- [ ] I care about others
- [ ] It will be okay
- [ ] I am okay
- [ ] I have good thoughts
- [ ] I am becoming better every day

How it helps

Do you know that most people have a nearly constant voice playing in their head like a tape stuck on replay? By paying attention to our self-talk, and changing it to supportive comments, we can change our habits and our feelings!

Write your best saying here, and decorate around it.

The Write Stuff

Writing a journal can help you put your worries
away, but keeping a diary isn't for everyone.
There are other things you can write that help
if you're having an anxious or sad spell.

Send a letter to someone you love. Write
it on paper, and draw around the edge.
Tell that person how you're feeling
inside, or just let them know what you
think about them. If you really enjoy
writing, send a letter to each member
of your family and put them under their
pillow to find as a surprise.

How it helps

Writing things down helps
your brain process the
thoughts and then leave
them alone. The simple
act of sitting quietly and
concentrating on the page
can be calming and positive.

Some people just LOVE writing lists. Try it for yourself and see if it's your new best thing. Here are some list ideas to get you started:

20 things that make me smile

My top 10 animals

3 jokes that make me laugh

5 famous people I admire

Places I would love to visit

Silly things I heard/saw today

Cloud Watching

Is your mind racing? Are your thoughts whirling around inside your head? Take time out and enjoy life at a slower pace for a while.

Find a safe space outside in the fresh air on a sunny day. Lie on your back, and watch the clouds above you. Do they make any familiar shapes? You might see animals, with ears or a tail. Perhaps you can see a gentle giant that lives in the sky, or a wizard casting a magic spell. You decide!

Close your eyes and feel the air on your skin. Is it warm air or cool air?

Can you tell when a cloud passes overhead even with your eyes closed? How?

Take time to notice as much as you can about the air around you.

What does air sound like?

How it helps

Being in nature makes you feel calmer and happier. It takes you away from human-made things and lets your mind have some time out. Looking at the clouds and noticing the air helps put your emotions in perspective. You'll stop hyper-focusing on your feelings and connect to the bigger universe.

Teddy Time

If people are getting on your nerves and you want to take time out,
take it with Teddy!

Lie down on your back and place a teddy on your belly. Breathe in deeply through your nose, and breathe out slowly. Watch how Teddy moves up and down. Does Teddy rise faster or slower than he falls? Does he stay up longer, or down longer? Does he stop at the top or at the bottom?

Take control of Teddy's ride. Can you make his ride smoother and calmer?

How it helps

Watching your teddy helps you see what your breathing looks like. That will help you focus on what your breathing <u>feels</u> like. The next time you need to control your breathing, you will know how to take a big, slow breath from deep inside your body.

Make it Rain

Sometimes the small things in life can make you happy, like the pitter patter of rain outside.

Make a rain stick so you can hear the lovely sound of gentle rain any time you like.

1 You will need a long, very strong card tube.

2 Push some tacks or nails into the tube. Spread them evenly around the tube. Secure them in place with tape.

3 Cover one end of the tube with paper, and seal it tightly with strong tape. You don't want it to break open.

4 Carefully pour in a cup of dry, uncooked rice.

5 Cover the other end of the tube and seal it with more tape.

6 Decorate the outside with giftwrap, foil, ribbons, or anything interesting you have lying around.

7 Now tip it on its end to hear the rice trickle down the tube. Turn it over again for the rice to run back.

How it helps

The sound of rain is a gentle and soothing noise. It can make you feel like you're tucked up safe and warm. The action of turning the rain stick over and over can be soothing, too!

Ask an adult to help you with the tacks or nails!

Close your eyes and imagine you're on a beautiful beach, listening to the waves gently breaking against the rocks.

Puppet Show

Do you find it difficult to try new challenges? Imagine yourself in another body to feel relaxed, flexible, and ready for anything.

You're going to pretend to be a puppet, just like Pinocchio.

1 Stand tall and strong with your arms at your sides. Plant your feet firmly on the floor, about hip distance apart. Breathe in deeply through your nose, and raise your shoulders up toward your ears.

2 Breathe out and drop your shoulders down again. Let your knees relax and nod your head. Now shake your head. Pinocchio says yes, and then no!

3 Droop forward like a puppet with no one holding the strings. Breathe in and out again, slowly.

4 Now imagine that your head has a string that is pulling you up, up, up toward the ceiling. Move your hands up to the sky as you breathe in at the same time.

Next, fold back down again into floppy Pinocchio position. Swing your arms as if your strings are loose again. Let your head hang loose, too.

Give your neck a break from all that work of holding up your head. Breathe in slowly. Let all your worries trickle out of your fingertips and onto the floor. Take a few deep breaths in this position, before slowly standing up straight. Think about how calm you feel.

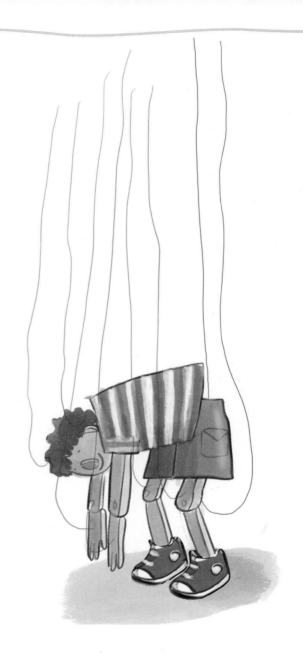

How it helps

Stretching your body like this helps to release tension and lets worries drift away. Lowering your head beneath your heart helps to control your body's response to stress.

Pebble Power

It can be reassuring to carry your own "calm stone" when you feel fidgety. Find it, feel it, fiddle with it … you can hold it in your pocket so no one else even knows it's there.

Ask a parent or guardian if you can look for calm stones. Look for them at the beach or near a river, where many of the pebbles have been smoothed by the water. The best ones are oval or round, and just bigger than the top half of your thumb. If you're lucky, you might find one that is shiny. Rub it between your fingers and thumb to check it gives you the best, most satisfying feeling.

You can make your own calm stone from oven-bake clay. Break off a small piece (or small pieces of a couple of different shades if you want to mix them up) and roll it into a ball between your palms. Gently squash it but don't flatten it completely. Press your thumb into one side to make a small hollow. Bake it in the oven following the instructions on the package

How it helps

Your calm stone will be there for you if you feel anxious or unsettled. Making small movements and focusing on touch can steer your brain away from negative thoughts. Handling your special stone will help you remember what it feels like to be chilled out. You can imagine that the stone is absorbing all of your fidgety, anxious energy, so you can be free to feel calm and at peace.

On Your Bike!

It's easy to spend the day on the couch but it won't help
you shake off feelings of worry or worthlessness.
You can change your mood with exercise—but you don't
need to join a gym!

1 Lie flat on the floor on your back.
Bend your knees so your feet are
flat on the floor.

2 Place your fingertips behind your
ears. Lift both feet off the floor
and slowly raise your knees.

3 Lift your head and shoulders slightly
so they aren't quite touching the
floor. Feel how your muscles are
working to hold your body in position.

4 Breathe out and pull your left knee
up toward your chest. Straighten the
other leg at the same time.

5 Breathe in, straightening the bent
leg and pulling up your right knee.

6 Repeat the action so it feels as if
you are riding a bike.

If you want to, twist at
the waist with each leg
movement so that your
opposite elbow nearly
touches your raised knee.

How it helps

Movement reduces nervous tension in your muscles, and so lessens anxiety in your body. Using your legs and stomach muscles to ride your imaginary bike burns off the worry chemicals that make you want to run away.

Set yourself an indoor training course. Run up and down the stairs ten times, and then do your on-the-floor cycling. If you don't have stairs run on the spot with high knees.

Finish up with a soak in the bathtub!

Teddy's Tale

What can you do when your body wants to sleep, but your head won't let it? Sometimes, lying in bed, your head is full of thoughts that keep you awake.

It's okay to lie awake for a while after you have turned off your electronics. Your brain needs time to unwind, as well as your body. Sometimes, though, when you stop doing other things, your mind fills up with worries that can keep you awake for too long.

If you have a trusty teddy, he can help. Snuggle him up close and ask him what he did today. Let your mind wander and invent an adventure with your teddy in the starring role. After a while, your mind should relax enough for you to drift into sleep.

What do teddies do when we're not there? Do they have exciting stories to tell?

If you're too old for a teddy, think about what you would do if you were making a movie with you in the lead role. Which places would you visit? What would you look like? Which friends would star with you? Would there be a bad guy? How would you teach him a lesson?

How it helps

Thoughts can be a good thing. We all need to think about things, to allow us to live our lives. Some thoughts turn to worries, and churn us up inside. Teach yourself to guide your thoughts into adventures, rather than things to be afraid of.

STOP!

Do you feel like life is moving too fast, or throwing too many things at you for you to handle? Take time out to get yourself together again.

You need to STOP:

Stop moving and be still, somewhere safe. Stand or sit, whichever you prefer.

Take a breath. Don't take big, deep breaths or hold your breath. Just focus on your normal breathing.

Observe. What is happening? Use your senses to listen, smell, and look around. What is going on inside your body and your head? How do you feel?

Proceed. You have taken time to think, and now it's fine to either carry on as you were, or make a change if that feels right.

How it helps

It can be hard to act in the right way if you're overwhelmed by things happening around you. Learning to take time out is a really good way to look after yourself.

When you reach the Proceed step, decide what you want to do based on how you are feeling. Did your Observe step tell you that you are hungry or thirsty? Have a healthy snack or a drink. Are you wound up? Use one of your calming techniques from this book. Maybe you need to focus on your breathing, or move around more.

Here are some feelings you might observe. Which are you feeling right now? Are there any more that you can add?

☐ Hungry   ☐ Tearful

☐ Tired   ☐ Empty

☐ Relaxed   ☐ Happy

☐ Joyful   ☐ Calm

☐ Lonely   ☐ Afraid

☐ Panicked   ☐ Amused

☐ Bored   ☐ Grateful

☐ Excited   ☐ Angry

☐ Overwhelmed   ☐ Relieved

☐ Full   ☐ Alive

☐ Loved   ☐ Pressurized

☐ Wobbly

Don't Forget

Do your emotions sometimes take over and make you act without thinking about others? It's easy to hide inside yourself and forget about being kind to other people.

1 Get out of your own head by making a beaded kindness reminder bracelet. Gather a selection of beads, big or small, and some thread.

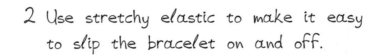

2 Use stretchy elastic to make it easy to slip the bracelet on and off.

3 Knot the thread at one end. Lay out the beads in a pattern that you like, and thread them on in order. Make a knot after last bead to keep them all in place.

If you prefer, use bigger beads. Feed them on to a pipe cleaner, and then twist the ends to make a loop.

> Why not make an identical bracelet to give to your best friend or sibling?

Twirl the beads in your fingers if you need to focus and concentrate. If you think you're acting thoughtlessly, or being mean, move the bracelet across to your other wrist. Move it back again if you act unkindly again. Swap it as a reminder to yourself, whenever you're not being kind.

Switch the bracelet from wrist to wrist if you need to be kinder to yourself, too.

How it helps

It is important to take notice of your actions. You don't need to get angry with yourself, just learn to see how you are behaving. Now you can make a decision—do you carry on the same way, or make a change?

Animal Poses

Do you find it hard to settle? Have you got twitchy legs or restless feet? Let the animals help you to relax.

Start by copying these stretches.

1 Stretch like a dolphin

2 Stand tall like a flamingo

3 Chill out like a turtle

4 Meow like a cat

How it helps

We often keep our stress inside our body, making our muscles tight and tense. Stretching helps to release the tension and make us more relaxed.

5 Moo like a cow

6 Lie down and stretch out your legs like a bug

What other animal shapes can you make your body copy?

Find Your Happy Place

Think of a place where you feel completely calm, happy, and safe. It might be somewhere you go all the time; somewhere you've only been once; somewhere you've seen in pictures; or somewhere you've completely made up.

It might be somewhere with a pretty view.

It can be inside or outside.

It might be the place that you play ball with your friends.

It might be a quiet reading spot.

Close your eyes, and imagine being in your happy place.
Imagine looking around. What can you see?
Are you alone, or with someone else? Draw or describe it here.

How it helps

Your mind is a powerful tool. The image of somewhere you love,
where you feel safe and calm, can really lift your spirits. Imagine
walking away from yucky anxious feelings to a peaceful place.

Get Your Glitter On

Are you feeling shaken up inside? Transfer those feelings to a gorgeously glittery jar and watch your worries settle down.

Make your own glitter jar.

1 Find a clean jar or bottle with a tight-fitting lid.

2 Fill it with warm water to about a third of the way up.

3 Squeeze in some glitter glue or clear glue, and then a drop of food dye and some ordinary glitter.

4 Stir it well and then add more warm water. It should be almost full, but leave a small gap so the mixture has room to move.

5 Make sure the lid is closed really, really tightly before you shake it!

Make sure you aren't holding your breath as you watch the glitter. That will re-fire your worry chemicals.

Take a breath inward as you shake the jar. Think about something that gets you swirled up inside. Breathe in and out slowly as the glitter settles. Watch and wait. The glitter will take its own time to fall; you can't rush it. Gradually, the jar will become clear again. Does your mind feel a little clearer too?

How it helps

Watching the glitter slowly fall down the jar has a soothing effect. It allows you to focus on something real in front of you, instead of thinking about what's going on elsewhere.

Pop Some Trouble Bubbles

Anxious thoughts can build up inside you and take over your body. Learn to blow your troubles into the air and let them float away.

1 In a clean jar or cup, mix a cup of water with 1/3 cup of dishwashing soap. You may need to experiment as some brands make better bubbles and some brands need slightly less water.

2 To make your bubble blower, bend a pipe cleaner or craft stem in half. Leave a thumb's length at the top and twist the rest together. Open out the top end into a loop. You can thread beads on to the handle to make it easier to hold.

3 Now dip the loop into the liquid, and blow gently to release a bubble.

Twist together two pipe cleaners to make a double bubble blower.

Ask a friend or family member to blow bubbles while you jump in the air and try to catch them or pop them. Can you blow enough bubbles for someone else to do the same?

How it helps

Blowing bubbles requires you to control your breath. If you blow too hard or too softly, the bubbles won't work. Breathing deeply and with focus is calming and makes you happy, too.

Whatever the Weather

If it rains a lot where you live, it can be hard to make yourself get outside to play. Yes, it's sometimes a pain having to change out of wet clothes, but rain can be fun too!

Put on clothes that are suitable for the weather, and then just get outside and feel the breeze on your face. Think about how it makes you feel. Can you catch the wind in your coat? Lift your face to the sky and let the sun warm your skin, or the rain fall on your cheeks.

Learn to embrace the weather, whatever it is doing. The planet needs sun, wind, and rain, and so do you!

How it helps

Different weather can calm and soothe us. Focus on the gentle patter of rain or the howling wind and recognize how toasty warm you are indoors.

The Goldilocks Game

Are things getting too much? Knowing your limits is important. Take a lesson from Goldilocks and figure out how much is too much, too little, or just right.

Stand up straight and raise one arm above your head. Now stretch that hand up as far as you can, as if you are trying to touch the clouds. Lower your arm and see how it feels. How does it compare to your other arm? Repeat with the other arm, and try to stretch even higher.

Now do it with both arms. How much is too far? How does it feel to be stretched too high? What are your muscles telling you? Do they ache? Do they need to rest?

Imagine that your best possession is perched on a shelf, just out of reach. How far would you stretch to try to get it back?

Notice your breathing as you stretch. Do you hold your breath as you over-reach? Does your breathing speed up? Is your body tingling?

How it helps

It can be easy to push yourself too far—to stay up too late, to play too long, to eat too much. Learning about how much is enough is a valuable lesson. There is a reason that the words "happy medium" are often put together, as just enough is a happy target to aim for.

Bake It Out

Work away your worries and stresses by baking bread. Research shows that baking can make you feel good about yourself and increase your happiness. And you get to eat the end result!

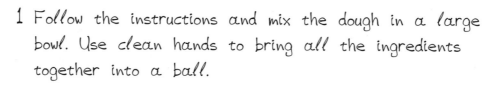

You will need a box of bread mix, or a recipe and your own ingredients.

1 Follow the instructions and mix the dough in a large bowl. Use clean hands to bring all the ingredients together into a ball.

2 Lift it out on to a floured surface, and pat a little more flour on to your hands so the dough doesn't stick.

3 Now knead the dough—use your knuckles to push the dough away from you and stretch it out. Now pull the farthest end back toward you, folding it over. Repeat this stretch—fold—stretch—fold again and again for 5 to 10 minutes.

4 Leave the dough in a bowl in a warm place, loosely covered with plastic wrap. It needs to rise and get bigger before you bake it.

5 Roll your bread into fist-sized balls to bake them.

6 With an adult's supervision, bake them in a hot oven until they are ready (make sure to use your recipe's instructions).

You could also roll two balls into long sausage shapes and twist together. You can spread pesto on one side or sprinkle with grated cheese for an extra-tasty treat. Experiment with different herbs and seeds to see which you and your family like best. Some to try are pizza seasoning, or poppy, sesame, or caraway seeds.

How it helps

The physical action of kneading dough uses your muscles and helps get rid of negative feelings. Paying attention to a new task keeps your brain focused. Making something you can be proud of, and that you can share with people you love, lifts your spirits.

Stress-Busting

Do you need to take time out and have a calm moment? It can be hard to just stop and chill out. Pick up your pencils and have fun with these pictures and patterns.

Choose the picture that appeals the most and make a start!

Drawing your own patterns can be very soothing. Find a piece of scrap paper and doodle away ...

How it helps

Drawing makes your brain concentrate on a single, creative task. It pushes other thoughts to the side while you relax and use your hands and fingers, focusing totally on the present moment.

Make a Mobile

Are you feeling stressed today? Take time out to make something that is pretty AND calming at the same time.

Make a mobile to hang over your bed, so you can lie back and watch it move in the air currents.

1 Use a paper plate, or cut a plate-sized circle from a cereal box.

2 Carefully cut inward from the outside edge, making a spiral.

3 Tie a piece of thread to the small inner section of the spiral. This is how you will hang up your mobile.

4 Cut out a selection of stars from card. Decorate with pens, or with stickers, ribbons, or giftwrap.

5 Loop together paper clips to make a chain. Thread one star at the bottom of the chain.

6 Make more chains with stars on. Attach them to the spiral at regular intervals, so they pull down the spiral and dangle.

How it helps

It can be hard to calm down without something to focus on. Simply lying on your bed might not be enough, but watching your mobile move around will allow your mind to settle on just one thing.

Befriend the Birds

It's incredibly soothing watching birds (or any wildlife!) going about their business. You can do this from inside your house, even if you live in a city, or when you're out to play or walking with your family.

Make a den for yourself next to a window. Gather pillows and blankets to make yourself comfortable. See how many birds you can spot. Watch what they are doing. Are they in pairs? Are they looking for food? What do they eat?

Try to identify the birds you see. Keep a tally chart so you know which types are the most frequent visitors, and which are special guests.

Keep a tally like this: ⵉⵉⵉⵉ |

ROBIN	
PIGEON	
BLACKBIRD	
SPARROW	

What else will you see?

How it helps

Modern life involves lots of things happening all at once, and that can be too much sometimes. Taking time to stop, sit, and concentrate on just one thing is good for you. Making a den and watching nature both have a soothing effect, too.

Wash Away Your Worries

Soothe away any tension with some imaginary water—all the rewards of a lovely, relaxing bath but without having to get wet.

Imagine a bucket filling up with warm rainwater. Breathe in while you count to five, slowly, and the bucket gets fuller and fuller. Now as you breathe out, imagine the water pouring out over your head and washing away all your worries. Let it trickle over you and carry your worries down to the ground. Feel the tension wash down your body and off past your feet with each outward breath.

The water makes you feel clean, warm, and happy, like these dolphins!

Where is your calm place? If you can imagine a bucket of rainwater washing over you, you can probably imagine yourself off in a faraway land. Would you love to be walking along the beach, or even swimming with whales? Your mind is a powerful tool so let it take you somewhere safe, warm, and worry-free.

How it helps

When you are anxious, your body changes state. Instead of being relaxed, your body is prepared to run away or stand and fight. By imagining water or a walk along the beach, you are taking yourself back into a calm state.

Full of Flowers

An anxious mind plays tricks on you. Do you sometimes worry that you aren't good enough, or that no one cares about you? Think of reasons to be thankful, and reach out to people around you for reassurance.

Gather together sheets of paper in various shades. Draw simple flower shapes onto them and cut them out. Copy the shapes here, if that helps.

Think of a happy happening and write it on one of the flowers. Did you help your friend understand her schoolwork? Maybe Grandma is coming for dinner? Perhaps Dad watched you on stage today? Stick the flower on the wall (with your parents' permission). See how your garden grows every time you add a happy happening!

You could try handing out flowers to your family and asking them to write their own happy happenings. It is interesting and fun to find out what makes other people happy.

If you're having a bad moment, go back to your flower garden and read the flowers. It will remind you of all you have to be grateful for and the weeds will be crowded out by the beautiful happenings in your life.

How it helps

Taking stock of the good parts of life can help lift your spirits. It isn't always easy to do, but keeping a flower wall acts as a good reminder.

One Thing at a Time

If you have lots of things to do, it can make you feel stressed. Which is the most important? How do you decide which to do first?

Imagine your list of things to do as pieces of a jigsaw puzzle. How do you do a jigsaw puzzle? One piece at a time!

Write down on each puzzle piece one thing that you have to do today. They might be big things (like football practice) or small things (like putting your school bag away or brushing your teeth), but write down everything that's important.

Now put them in order. Think about which things absolutely must be done, and which can wait. Use a pencil to write down a little (1) next to the thing you definitely need to do first.

If it doesn't matter which order some of the things have to be done in, decide which you'd prefer to do, and then put that in the highest spot available.

When you've worked out roughly what order they should be in, rewrite the list of things to do here, in order. Now it's time to get busy! Try to forget about the rest of the list while you do one thing at a time.

How it helps

Writing things down helps you translate your thoughts into words. Once things are written down you can see and evaluate what needs to be done and how important each thing might be. You will also have a visual reminder so you won't have to waste energy worrying that you will forget or miss something.

Give Yourself a Head Start

Begin your morning in the best possible frame of mind
by getting ready for the next day before you go to bed.

Zzz... *Zzz...*

Before you get tucked in, pack your backpack for the next day with any things you might need for school. If you take a packed lunch or snacks to school, prepare them and leave them in the refrigerator overnight. Find a full set of clothes (including underwear and socks and shoes) and place them neatly somewhere in your room.

Zzz.....

Children aged between 6 and about 12 need about 10 to 11 hours' sleep every day. That means if you need to get up at 7 to get ready for school, you should be in bed (and ready to sleep, not watch screens or read!) at about 8pm.

When you wake up in the morning, make sure to say hello to your family, and eat a good breakfast. You're ready for the day ahead—today will be a good day!

How it helps

Getting a good start to the day is really helpful for people who struggle with anxiety. If you know you won't need to run around looking for things or making decisions in the morning, you're more likely to get a good night's sleep, too!

Reality Check

Some things that you might be worried about are definitely going to happen (like a new school week or a test), but you might be afraid of something that is very unlikely to happen—and what's the point of that!

Think about your worries and sort them into these two lists.

LIST 1:
Things that might actually happen

If you're worried about something that is likely to happen (like getting hungry on a long trip), try to make a plan to make it as easy on you as possible (like packing a couple of healthy snacks).

LIST 2:

Things that are very unlikely to happen

_____

_____

_____

_____

_____

_____

_____

_____

_____

_____

_____

If something you've been worrying about isn't likely to happen, try to imagine letting the worry go, like letting go of a balloon.

How it helps

Putting things into perspective helps you use your energy in a productive way. If something you are frightened of is likely to happen, spend some time planning how you can make it easier. If something's probably not going to happen, you can choose to spend your time doing something more fun than worrying!

Prediction Experiment

If you find yourself worrying a lot about everyday things, try writing down your specific worries, and then check back after a week or so to see if your worries came true.

Write three things that you're worried might happen this week:

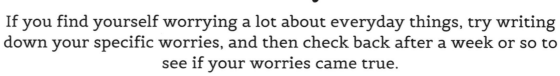

A week later, look back at your worries on page 84. Did they come true? Were things as bad as you thought they might be?

The results are in!

How it helps

Sometimes we worry out of habit. If your worry predictions didn't come true, perhaps that's a worry you can stop thinking about?

For Parents

Why is your child anxious?

All children experience some worries, fears, and anxious feelings now and again. It's our job as parents and caregivers to help children learn how to handle their worries in a healthy way.

The ideas in this book help your child slow down their stress response so that they gain control over choosing their thoughts, feelings, and actions.

Children who are worried sometimes feel very alone and don't know that other people have the same feelings. A listening ear and support from you goes a long way in helping your child realize that everyone feels anxious sometimes.

Symptoms of Anxiety

Anxiety is a very real problem for everyone nowadays. Children and adults alike live their lives at a fast pace and under large amounts of pressure from those around us.

Anxiety can manifest itself in a variety of ways, and can present differently in individual children, including siblings. Your child might struggle with hot flushes, clammy hands and feet, or needing to go the toilet more than normal. They may feel their heart is racing or that they are short of breath. Nerves can cause butterflies in the belly or a dry mouth, but also more severe symptoms such as dizziness, shaking, headaches, and nausea.

Mentally, your child may be overthinking, leading to tooth-grinding, problems falling asleep or staying asleep, and even panic attacks. Anxiety can make a child feel disconnected, out of touch with reality, or that everyone is looking at them. They may need extra reassurance, either that things are going to be okay or that they haven't done anything to upset people. It can seem like the world is slowing down or speeding up. They may even worry about the worrying, and that something bad will happen if they let their attention slip even slightly. It all takes its toll and is extremely hard work for a child to carry around with them.

For Parents

What Is Anxiety?

Anxiety is one of the basic human emotions. Its purpose is to keep us unharmed and alive.

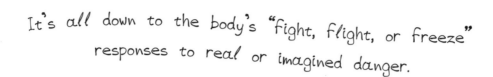

It's all down to the body's "fight, flight, or freeze" responses to real or imagined danger.

When a person feels under threat, their body prepares to run, or stand and face the danger. Their heart begins to beat faster to pump blood into their muscles. This deprives the brain of oxygen, causing a dizzy or light-headed feeling. The liver releases sugar to give an energy boost, which can make people feel fidgety and restless. As the body prepares to flee or freeze, it sacrifices other less important tasks such as digesting food. That's why the mouth feels dry (no saliva is produced) and the stomach feels sick or full of butterflies. The body wants to evacuate any unnecessary weight, resulting in additional trips to the toilet.

An anxious person's mind becomes alert and ready to face the situation, but if there is not a concrete problem to solve, action to take, or anything to actually worry about, it can lead to overthinking. It becomes hard to relax, as they feel the need to stay alert to deal with problems, even if they are imaginary or exaggerated. They begin to think that possible scenarios are reality, and their mind buzzes with ways to find solutions.

When the fight, flight, or freeze response is triggered, your child's body is being flooded with adrenaline, norepinephrine, and cortisol. These powerful chemicals produced in their body are designed to give a boost to perception, reflexes, and speed in dangerous situations. The chemicals increase your child's heart rate, bring blood to their muscles, get more air into their lungs, and make their senses vigilant.

Your child turns their full attention to survival. The stress response is designed to shut down as the threat passes and their body goes back to normal. This usually takes about 20-60 minutes. And your child might feel very tired and even fall asleep afterwards. You have probably noticed your child's stress responses can get derailed, stuck, or even re-ignited at times. The getting stuck can happen in the thinking, emotion, or physical part of the reaction.

Anxiety is part of your child's stress response. It is more than just a feeling. It is made up of thoughts, feelings, and physical changes that are all tied together in a biochemical feedback loop that together can make each other stronger or more intense ... and can lead your child to getting stuck. Introducing the practical recommendations in this book into their daily routine should help your child get unstuck.

For Parents

How you can help

Learning emotional regulation is a life-long journey, and you play a vital role in your child's development.

1 Do a basic needs check
Is your child hungry, tired, sick, frustrated, or bored? Sometimes a simple snack, an early bedtime, changing an activity, or tucking them under a cozy blanket may be all that is needed.

2 Lend a listening ear
Sometimes sad feelings take on a life of their own and the child can no longer identify what caused their sadness. Help them make a list of the times when they felt calm. Focus on those for a few minutes. Let them know that you are there to listen if they want to talk. When your child does talk to you, be sure that you are receptive to how they are feeling. Don't brush it aside or tell them not to worry. Instead, let your child know that it's okay to feel upset, but that you can look for solutions together. Follow your child's lead and ask open-ended questions.

3 Be a supportive presence
Physical contact can go a long way to soothe an anxious child. A good hug releases oxytocin which promotes feelings of connection and bonding. Alternatively, sitting shoulder-to-shoulder when talking or reading together may be the right amount of physical contact for your child. Follow your child's lead and respond sensitively.

4 Encourage movement
Remember that we are made for movement. Moving our muscles literally lifts our spirits by stimulating the release of feel-good hormones like serotonin. What the movement is doesn't matter, so if your child feels like riding a bike, going for a swim, or digging a hole in the backyard for a fairy pond, support them in doing it. The positive feelings generated by exercise can drive out negative ones.

5 Drink plenty of water
Teach your child the importance of drinking water throughout the day. Dehydration can affect our mood as well as our brain function and physical performance.

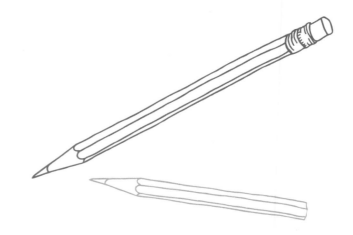

6 Limit exposure to negative stimuli

Research shows that watching TV shows with arguing, fighting, shooting, car accidents, ridicule, death, and loss affect the viewer's brain as if they experienced these things directly. Have your child limit their viewing of TV and get them to generate his or her own entertainment through making puppet shows, writing stories, or playing charades. When they do need "down time" play pleasant instrumental music, or have them do a puzzle, draw, or read. These activities bring a great sense of peace, and diminish preoccupation with sad storylines.

For Parents

How you can help (continued)

7 Good sleep and regular diet

Ensure that your child is well fed and well rested. Good nutrition and a regular sleep pattern are vital for a growing child, particularly one who is struggling with anxious feelings. A child aged 6–12 needs 10–11 hours sleep every night. Eat healthy food and occasional treats together as a family.

8 Happy energy is contagious

Cheerful parents tend to create optimistic home environments. Parenting an unhappy child can be exasperating and stressful. There is no shame in struggling with feeling down yourself. Find another adult to talk to and engage in some self care. If you are able to keep your cool and lighten the mood by not taking everything too seriously, allow yourself to be silly and laugh. By watching you, your child will gain perspective on the intensity of their brooding feelings and may be able to laugh, too.

9 Let them be kids!

Don't overload their childhood days with clubs and lessons. Have faith in their schooling and the professionals who know how hard children should be working at their age. Allow your kids time to play and unwind, and encourage them to spend time with their peers and siblings. Try to allow them some totally unstructured time most days, and let them do anything they would like, provided that it is safe, doesn't inconvenience you, and is within your budget.

10 Bring in reinforcements!

Your child may benefit from talking to someone else they trust. Point them in the direction of a teacher, a relative, or a helpline with trained counsellors. Exposure to a wide variety of viewpoints will give your child the best chance of responding to a point of view that clicks with them. They might (or might not) talk to an aunt or friend of yours. Let your child help out a relative with a task, and see if they start chatting.

11 Help your child set a small goal

Lazing about breeds sour feelings when you are down. Achieving a goal does wonders for morale. Pick out an activity from this book and help your child get started. Simple beading and baking projects lead to a sense of accomplishment, as does tidying up a drawer.

12 Set a routine

Routine is important in helping children to feel safe and grounded. A good morning routine will set the tone for the day. Get up early enough to avoid chaos and fluster; eat a good breakfast; go through what they need so they feel supported and prepared for the day ahead. Bedtime routines are equally comforting, and can include stretches and a bedtime story to settle them both physically and mentally.

13 And finally,

Take care of yourself, too. Parenting a child with big worries can be exhausting and lonely. Remember to take care of yourself and get support when you need it. Parenting is tough work at times and you don't have to go it alone. You may find joining a parent group, finding talks on parenting, or even working with a therapist helpful. The stronger and healthier your are, the more capable and calm your child will feel.

Glossary

anxious
To feel uneasy, fearful, or worried.

clammy
Sweaty.

cooped up
To feel closed in.

current
A flow of air or water.

electronics
Another word for devices, such as a phone, tablet, or gaming device.

evaluate
To assess or figure out the value of something.

frame of mind
Another phrase like "state of mind" that means your mood or attitude to something.

homeostasis
Feeling content, stable and balanced.

hyper-focusing
To concentrate on something intensely.

keyed up
To feel wound up, tense, or agitated.

nervous energy
An uneasy, jittery feeling that makes you want to move or do something.

perspective
A way of looking at something.

pesto
A sauce made from basil, cheese, oil, and pine nuts.

prediction
To say what is going to happen in the future.

pressurized
To be or to feel squeezed or pressed.

productive
To get things done.

pulse
The beats of your heart.

reassurance
A way to relieve worry and give confidence.

reflective
To think about yourself, your feelings and actions.

regulating
Adjusting.

sibling
A brother or sister.

tally chart
A grid showing a score or count.

tension
When something is stretched, pulled beyond its normal state.

thermostat
A device to turn the temperature up or down.

threat
A danger or something you think might cause you harm.

unbalanced
To feel unstable or unsteady in body or mind.

withdrawn
To detach yourself from others or a situation, either physically or in your mind.

worthlessness
A feeling of being unimportant.

Further Reading

Many excellent resources are available to support you and your child. If you need advice and information on a specific concern, start by consulting your family doctor or a child psychologist.

Below are a few books, websites, and community resources for you to explore.

My Family Divided: One Girl's Journey of Home, Loss, and Hope Written by Diane Guerrero with Erica Moroz

In My Heart: A Book of Feelings Written by Jo Witek, illustrated by Christine Roussey

My Many Colored Days Written by Dr. Seuss, illustrated by Steve Johnson and Lou Fancher

Tough Guys (Have Feelings Too) Written and illustrated by Keith Negley

When Sophie Gets Angry — Really, Really Angry… Written and illustrated by Molly Bang

How to Talk So Kids Will Listen and Listen So Kids Will Talk by Adele Faber and Elaine Mazlish.

Parenting from the Inside Out: How a Deeper Self-Understanding Can Help You Raise Children Who Thrive by Daniel J. Siegel and Mary Hartzwell.

North America

kidshealth.org
With sections for parents, kids, and teens, this is what most pediatricians use for education.

www.girlshealth.gov
A website specifically for girls, this has lots of great information about feelings, relationships, and biology.

healthfinder.gov
Mostly for parents, this has lots of good advice articles.

adaa.org
The specific website of the Anxiety and Depression Association of America.

worrywisekids.org
Accessible to both kids and adults, this is a great source of information on anxiety and depression.

UK

Childline
Help and advice about a huge range of issues. Comforts, advises, and protects children 24 hours a day, and offers free, confidential counselling by helpline, online chat, and Ask Sam. Tel: 0800 1111 www. childline.org.uk

The Samaritans
Listening and support for anyone who needs it. Contact 24 hours a day, 365 days a year—calls and emails are free and confidential. Tel: 116 123 www.samaritans.org

NHS
www.healthforkids.co.uk/feelings/
You can always talk to your family GP about your feelings.

Australia & New Zealand

Kids Helpline (telephone and online counselling for ages 5-25)
kidshelpline.com.au/ or call 1800 55 1800

Youthline
www.youthline.co.nz
Free call 0800 376 633
Free text 234

Index

A
adrenaline 88
anger 13, 22, 28–29
animals 24–25, 54–55, 72–73
anxiety 4–5, 8, 18, 86–89
    definition 88–89
    management 4
    symptoms 5, 87, 88

B
baking 30–31, 66–67
bath times 47
bedtimes 48–49, 93
bodies, listening to 8, 10–13, 20–21
bracelets, kindness 52–53
bread making 66–67
breathing techniques 16–17, 24,
    38–39, 42–43, 50, 60–61, 74
bubbles, blowing 60–61
butterflies 13, 87–88

C
calm stones 44–45
chemicals 10, 29, 47, 88
chest exercises 18
cloud watching 36–37
cortisol 88
crafts 68–71, 76–77

D
dehydration 90
diary-keeping 34
diet 92
drawing 68–69, 76–77

F
fear 4, 22
feelings/emotions 4–5
    goals 6–7
    management 4, 5, 7, 24–25,
    28–29, 90–91
    recognizing 5, 8, 13, 20–23,
    50–51

"fight, flight, or freeze" response
    75, 88
flexibility, mental 42–43

G
glitter jars 58–59
goal-setting 6–7, 93

H
happy/calm places 56–57, 75
heart rate 14–15, 87–88
homeostasis 9

K
kneading 66–67

L
letter writing 34
limits, knowing your 64–65
list-making 35, 82
listening skills 90

M
mind 57, 59
mobiles 70–71
moods, changing 8–9
morning routines 80–81, 93
muffins 30–31

N
nature 26–27, 36–37, 40–41,
    44–45, 62–63, 72–73
needs, basic 90
negativity 32, 67, 91
nervousness 4, 13, 87
norepinephrine 88

O
overthinking 87, 88
oxytocin 90

P
parents' guide 86–93
pebbles 44–45
physical exercise 14–15, 18–19,
    46–47, 54–55, 90
prediction experiment 84–85

R
rain 40, 62–63
rain sticks 40
reality checks 82–83
ribbon dancing 29
routines 80–81, 93

S
sadness 5, 22
self-care 93
self-talk 32–33
sensations 10, 12–13, 22–23
serotonin 90
skin 20–21
sleep 80, 87, 92
STOP test 50–51
stress response 88–89
stretches 54–55
support 5, 87, 90–93

T
talking things through 5
teddies 38–39, 48–49
tension, releasing 18–19, 43, 47,
    55, 74
threat perception 88
time out 50–51

W
water
    drinking 90
    imaginary 74–75
worries 4, 49, 58, 76, 82–85
writing things down 34–35,
    78–79, 84–85